BHIMAYANA

BHIMAYANA

incidents in the life of

BHIMRAO RAMJI AMBEDKAR

art
DURGABAI VYAM, SUBHASH VYAM

story
SRIVIDYA NATARAJAN, S. ANAND

type design
APARAJITA NINAN

chapter headings
ROSHNI VYAM

curation and design
S. ANAND

production
SANJIV PALLIWAL

navayana

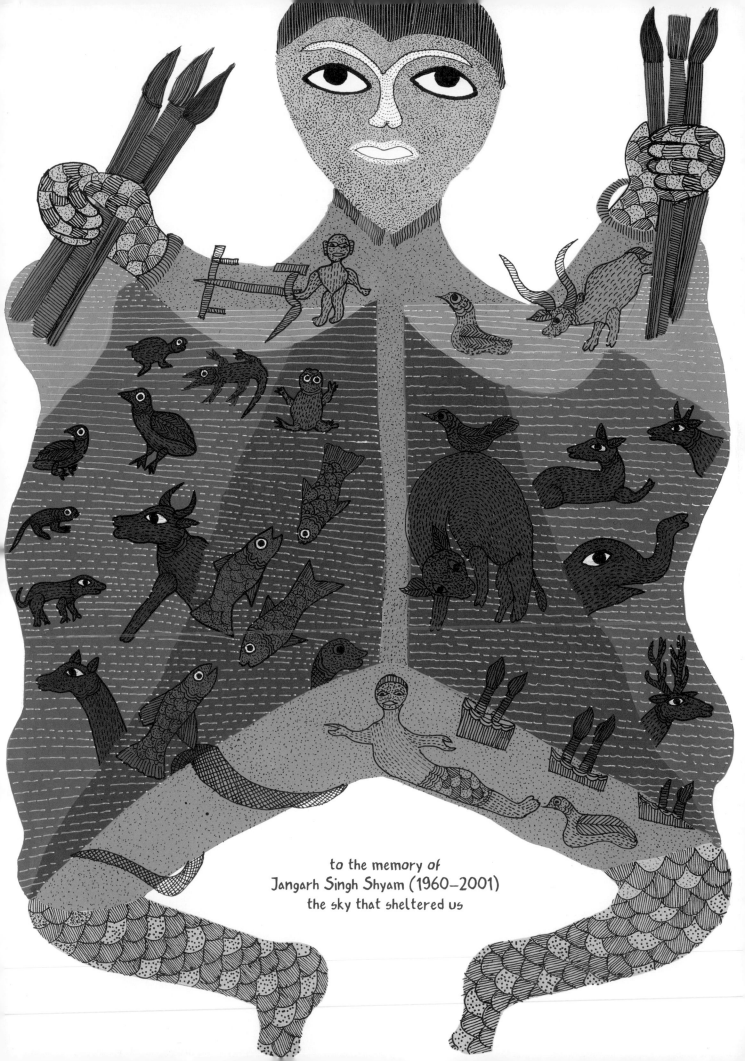

to the memory of
Jangarh Singh Shyam (1960–2001)
the sky that sheltered us

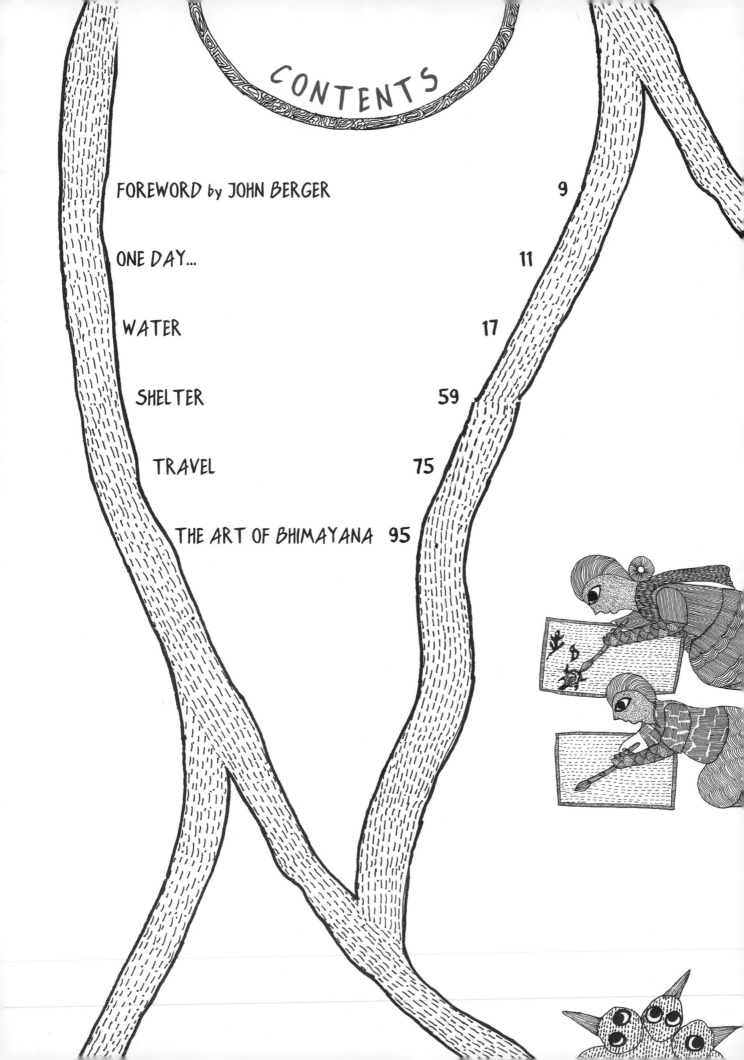

CONTENTS

FOREWORD

I want to try to say something about the way this extraordinary book tells its story.

During the 19th and 20th centuries History was confronted and visualized as a stage: a stage on which women and men struggled to choose and achieve their destiny and a life in which there was more justice; their struggles were inspired and accompanied by the words of visionaries, political thinkers and active politicians, some of them wielding power, others subversive. Such an Historical stage with its proscenium arch, its regular seats set out as in an amphitheatre, its dramatic lighting and acoustics, was present in poems, written stories, political meetings, insurrections, songs, shared dreams. Today no longer.

The imagined theatre has been destroyed by so-called Communication Experts, the media, politicians without a future, and a global economic system which reduces the whole of History and every horizon of life to the pursuit of profit. On the site of the stage there is today a Shopping Mall.

Yet, in fact, History continues and the struggles persist. And so we face the challenge of how to tell stories about them across the world today.

This book offers a prophetic answer and it is this: replace the stage of History with the Body of a community. A body with a long past, a present of many voices, and a vision of the future. Reading the book and following its story, we enter this body, its bloodstream, its organs, its members.

No more proscenium arch. No more rectangular framing or unilinear time. No more profiled individuals. Instead, a conference of corporeal experience across generations, full of pain and empathy, and nurtured by a complicity and endurance that can outlive the Market.

Stories are being told like this all over the world. They are seldom printed and published. This book has now set an example.

Let us thank everyone who contributed to it for that example.

JOHN BERGER
26 July 2010
Taninges, France

ONE DAY IN THE RECENT PAST, A BUS STOP IN AN INDIAN CITY...
Super-qualified. Stuck in a dead-end job. That's my life...
I blame these damn job **quotas** for Backward and Scheduled Castes. It isn't fair!
Well... caste isn't fair.

TENSION AFTER DALITS DRAW WATER FROM WELL

KOLHAPUR, HINDUSTAN TIMES, 29 SEPT 2010

On the face of it, Ghungurwadi village in Shahuwadi Taluk, Maharashtra, named after social reformer King Rajashri Shahu Maharaj, should be setting an example for the upliftment of the socially downtrodden. But dalits here are still subjected to discrimination. On September 20, one act of the dalits from Ghungur put an end to nearly 60 years of discrimination. Narsu Kamble, his cousin Sugriv Kamble, along with several other members of the community, fetched drinking water from a well meant for the Marathas. Irked, members of the upper caste denounced the act and boycotted the water from the well.

Two dalit teenagers were assaulted, tied with ropes and then dragged for several meters by a group of villagers in Uttar Pradesh's Rae Bareli district on charges of stealing a mobile phone kept in a vehicle, police said Monday. Ajai Nat (15) and Ravishankar Raidas (14), residents of Lachminia village, some 80 km from Lucknow, were accused of stealing a mobile phone on Sunday evening from the truck of Balbir Singh, who has a transport business in the village. When Singh failed to recover the mobile from them, he called three of his associates, and together they beat up the teenagers with wooden sticks and also shaved their heads. Thereafter, both the teenagers were tied with ropes and dragged for several meters in the village. "We came to know about the incident on

HONOUR KILLING SHOCKS THE CAPITAL
NEW DELHI, MAIL TODAY, 15 JUNE 2010

In an incident that could send shockwaves across the Capital, a 19-year-old girl and her boyfriend were allegedly bludgeoned and electrocuted to death by her family in Swaroop Nagar in north-west Delhi around midnight on Sunday. Asha Saini and her [dalit] boyfriend Yogesh Jatav (also 19) were kept away from each other by the girl's family after their relationship was discovered. Both were reportedly from different castes. Asha, a resident of Gokulpuri in north-east Delhi, was sent to her uncle Om Prakash's house in Swaroop Nagar around a fortnight ago but Yogesh managed to somehow meet his girlfriend on Sunday night.

ROW OVER 'UNTOUCHABLE' INDIAN DOG
MORENA (MADHYA PRADESH), BBC NEWS, 24 SEPT 2010

Police in India are investigating claims that a dalit woman has been ordered to pay compensation to the high-caste owners of a dog she fed. The woman says the village council wants her to pay a fine of 15,000 rupees ($330) for feeding the dog, which the owners have now kicked out. The incident took place in Malikpur village in Morena district in central Madhya Pradesh state. "I made some roti and took it into my husband who works in a farm. After I had fed him we had some leftovers which I gave to the dog," the dalit woman, Sunita Jatav, said. She said the owner of the dog, Amruttal Kirari, saw her feeding him. "He got very angry and said 'You've fed my dog so it has become an untouchable now.'" Mrs Jatav said Mr Kirari left the dog, a black mongrel called Sheru, tied to a pole outside her house. On Monday, they

JUST ANOTHER RAPE STORY
SABRINA BUCKWALTER
TIMES OF INDIA, 29 OCT 2006

The village of **Khairlanji**, near Nagpur, is an unremarkable settlement of brick huts and cement houses. Less than 200 families live here. Dirt roads run between flat farmlands, and the eye sees great sprawling distances. There was always a gaping silence in this village, even before September 29 when an upper caste mob, according to eyewitnesses, paraded a mother and her 17-year-old daughter naked, raped and killed them. Two other members of the family, brothers aged 19 and 21, too were murdered. Their bodies were dumped in a canal. Thirty-eight men have been arrested and they are being held in police custody. The gruesome incident occurred **780 km from Mumbai**, too far out it appears to muster national outrage. The news of this brutality did not enter the mainstream news in any significant fashion...

DALIT KILLED FOR DEMANDING WAGE

A dalit in a Madhya Pradesh village only wanted payment of wages due to him—but what he got was death. Mason Ramesh Jatav was allegedly killed after

TIMES NATION
Untouchability alive & kicking in India
Dalits Have Little Access To Temples, Their Kids Are Made To Sit Separately In Schools

THE TIMES OF INDIA, NEW DELHI
MONDAY, AUGUST 3, 2009

BOOK 1

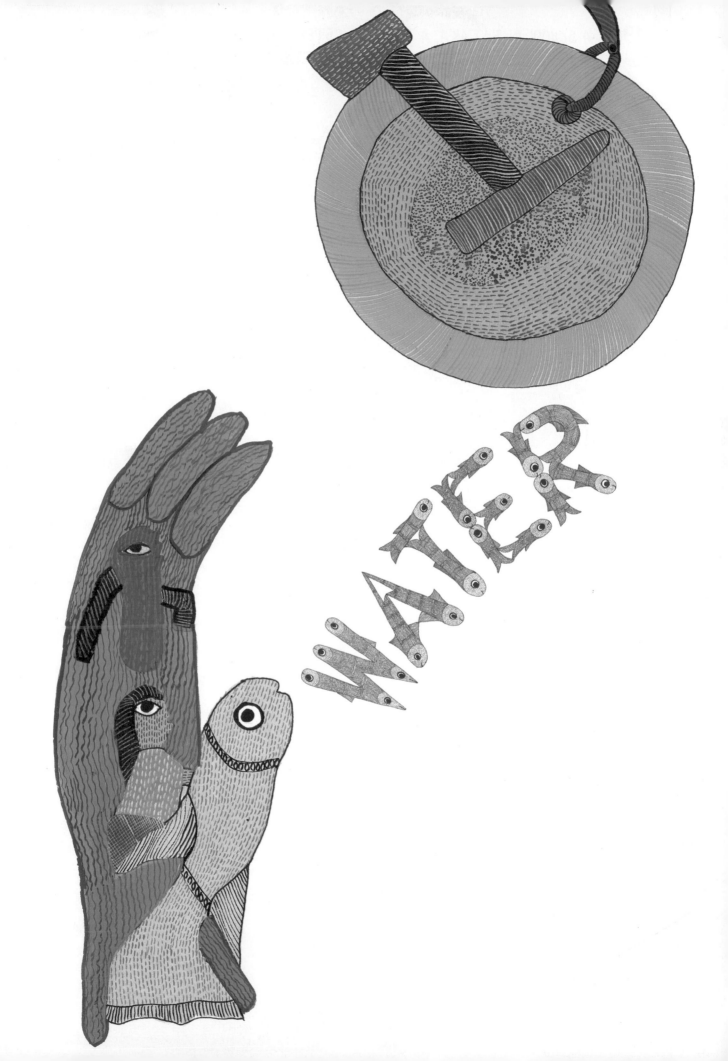

1901. A SCHOOL IN SATARA, A TOWN IN WESTERN INDIA.

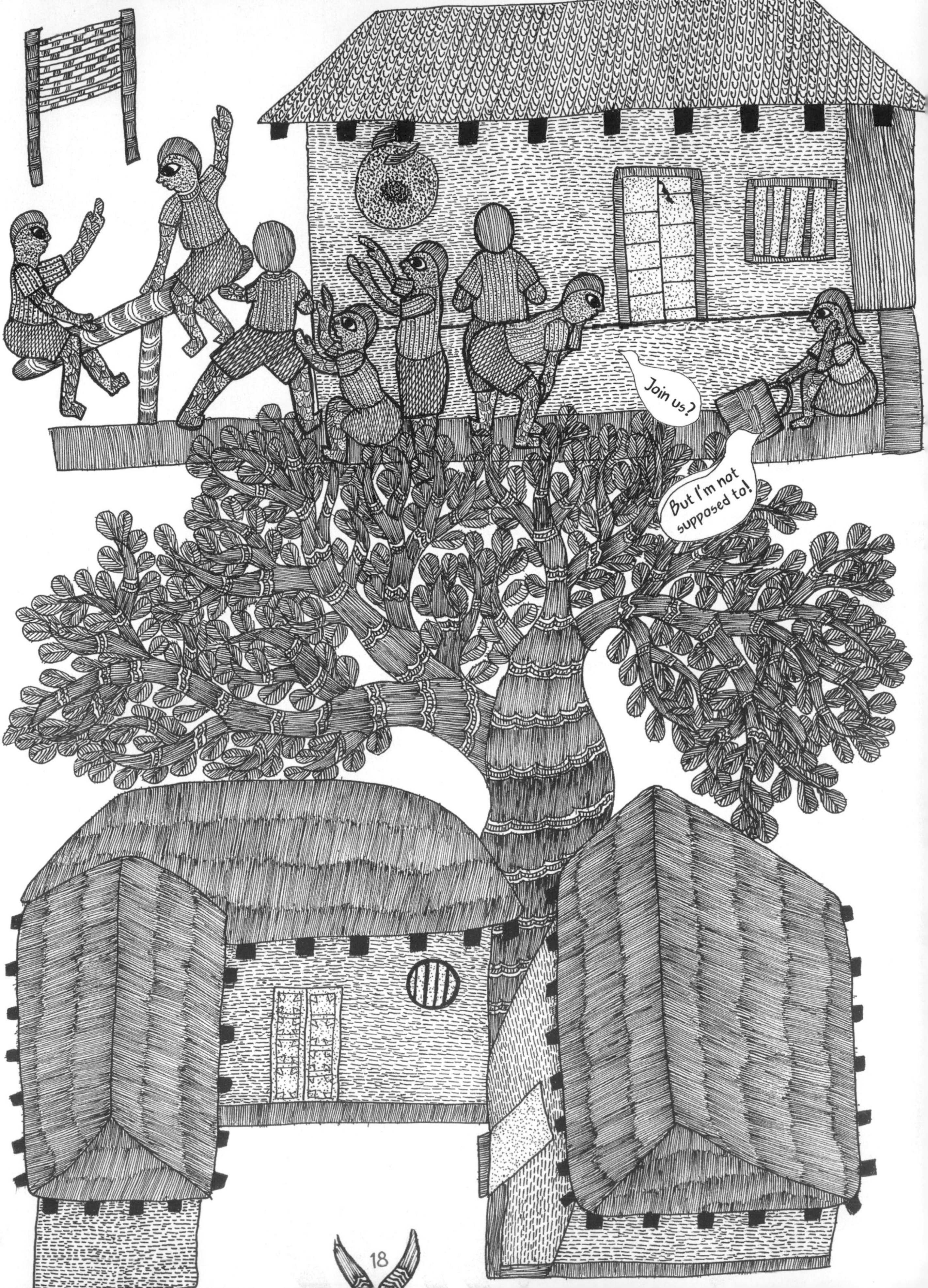

THEY HAVE BRUSHES FOR THE BUFFALO AND SHEARS FOR THE GOAT,
THEY WON'T TRIM A MAHAR'S HAIR — THEY'D RATHER CUT HIS THROAT.

BOYS AT THE WELL, EVEN BEASTS AT THE TROUGH,
MAY DRINK TILL THEY BURST,
BUT THE VILLAGE TURNS A DESERT
WHEN I TRY TO QUENCH MY THIRST.

25

WEEKS LATER...

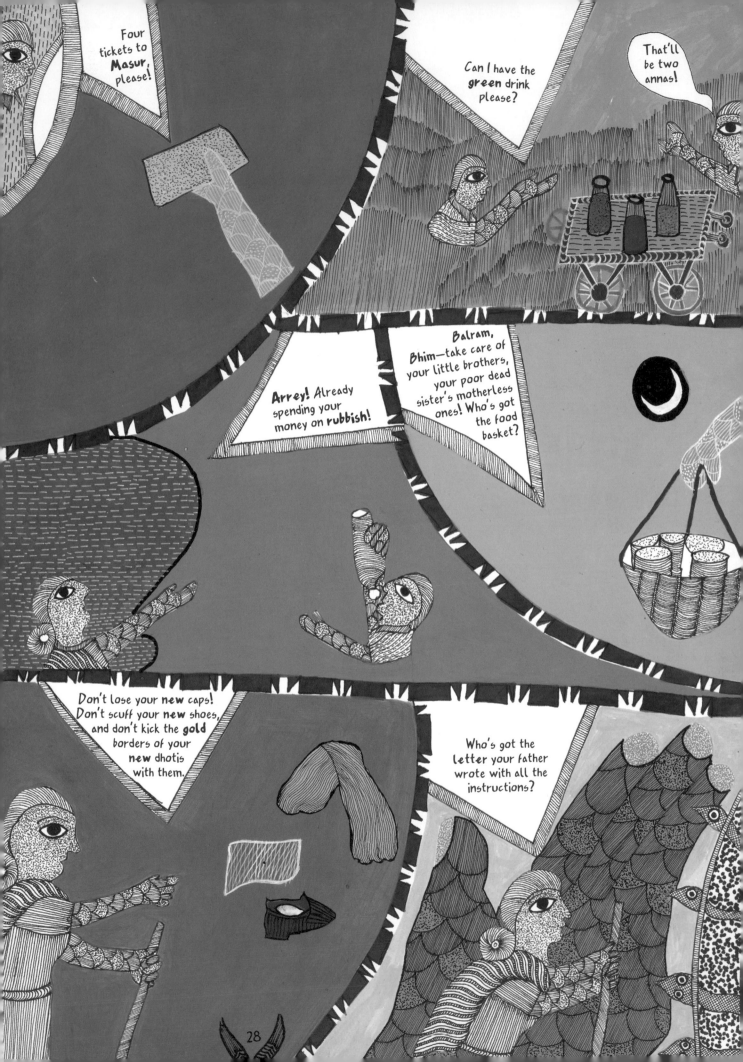

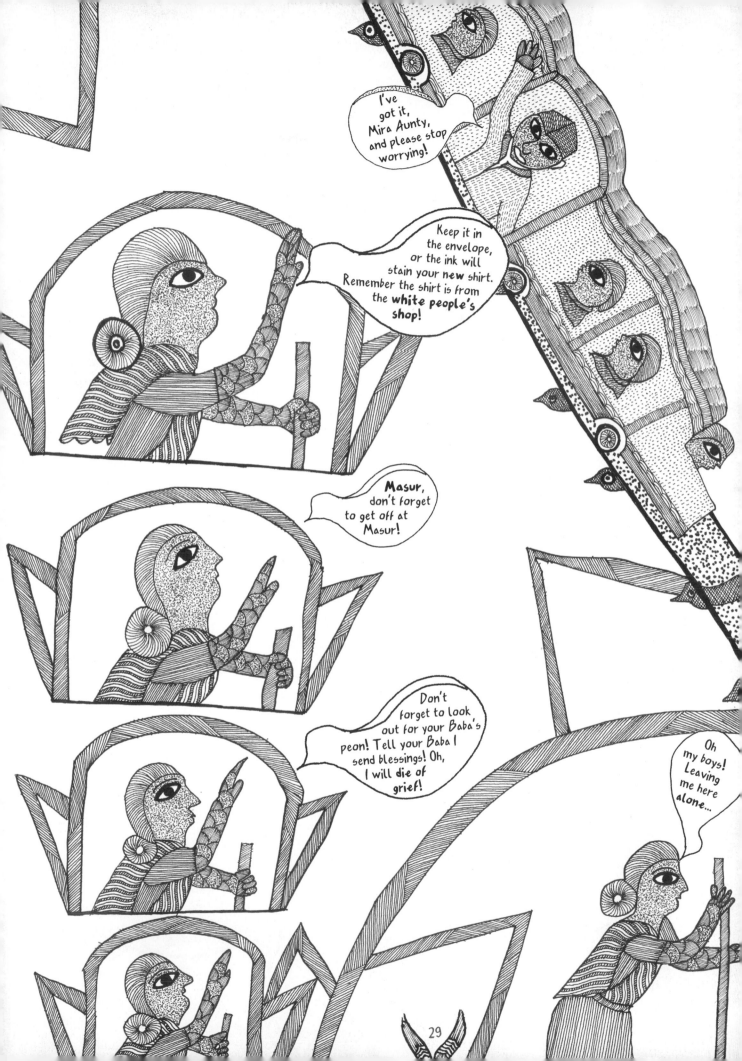

29

TOWNS WITH MAGICAL NAMES FLASH BY—
BHIM'S HEART IS A BIRD IN A CLOUDLESS SKY.

31

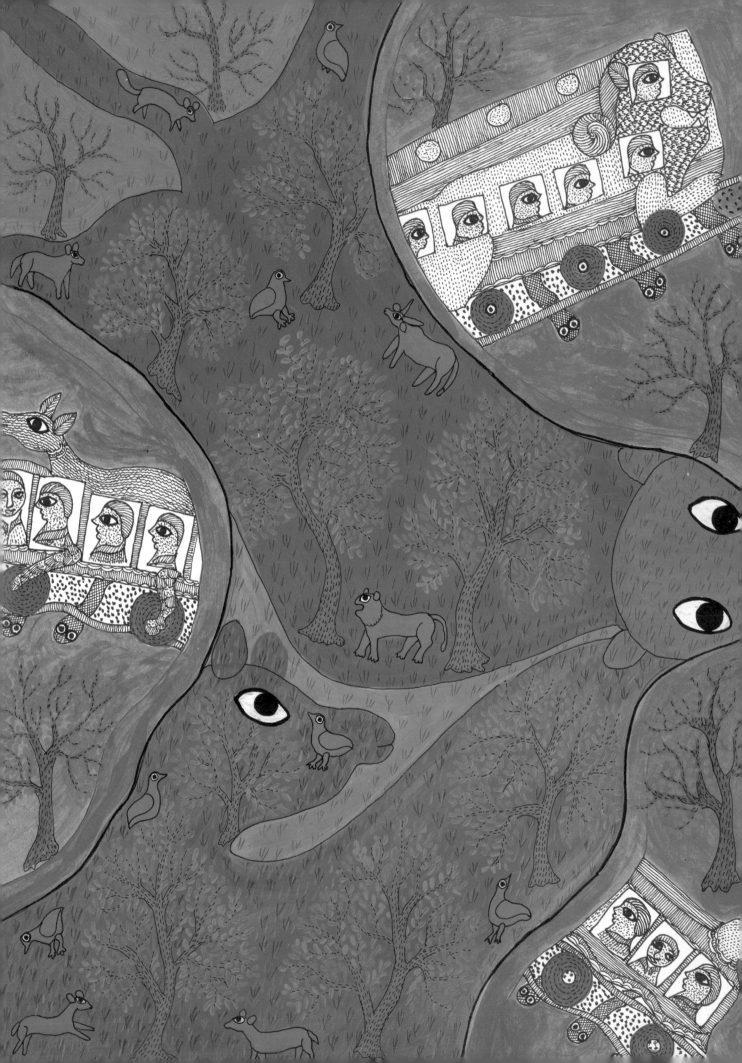

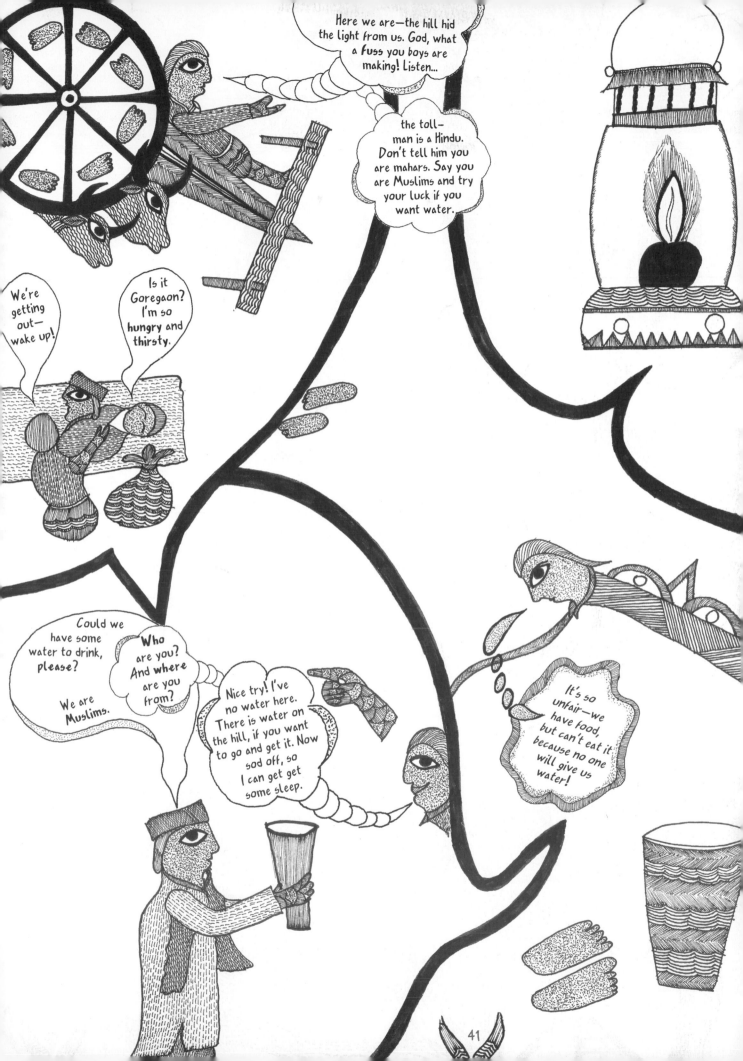

41

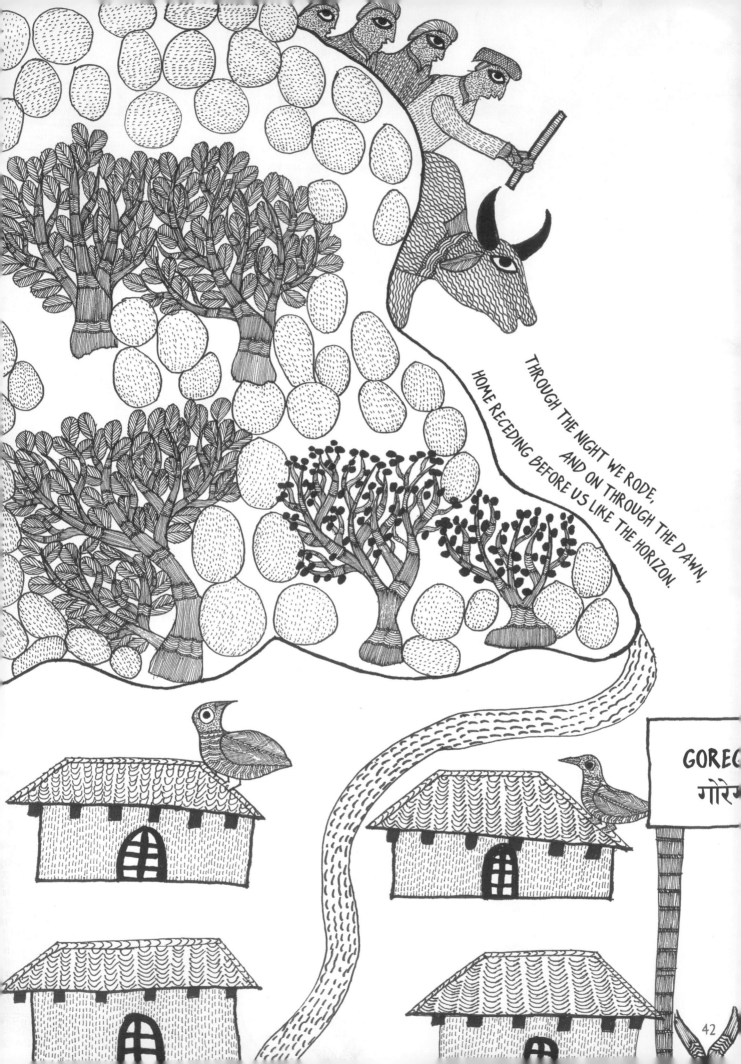

THROUGH THE NIGHT WE RODE,
AND ON THROUGH THE DAWN,
HOME RECEDING BEFORE US LIKE THE HORIZON.

GOREG
गोरेग

42

46

DALIT KILLED FOR DIGGING OWN WELL

HINDUSTAN TIMES
SATARA, 4 MAY 2008

Gautam (name changed) is a police constable in Satara's Man taluka, but even he could not save his brother-in-law Madhukar Ghatge.

Ghatge (48), a dalit farmer and a father of three, retired from the Railways a few years ago and moved home from Mumbai to farm on his family's 5-acre plot here. He was murdered last week by upper-caste villagers who did not want him to dig a well on his own property.

It would have been the first well in Kulakjai village on land owned by a dalit.

The police said Ghatge was hacked so violently that even the earth-moving machine he was using at the time was damaged.

"They left him to die. They were armed with axes and iron rods. They attacked him and left him to bleed to death," said Ghatge's 21-year-old son Tushar, a law student at a local college.

WATER WARS: DALIT WOMAN TORCHED

TIMES OF INDIA
BHOPAL, 6 JUNE 2008

An elderly dalit woman was burnt alive allegedly by three members of an upper caste community over a dispute on fetching water from a village handpump in a Madhya Pradesh village.

Prembai, 55, suffered 80 percent burns as she was set ablaze on Tuesday, Abhishek Ranjan, sub-divisional police officer, said on Friday.

The incident took place at Harda's Kantada village where Prembai was stopped from using the village handpump by three upper caste persons, Ranjan said.

"A quarrel erupted as she refused to budge, following which Hiralal, Dinesh and Rajendra allegedly set her on fire," he said, adding, "Prembai succumbed to burn injuries on Wednesday."

That's **crazy**, that's **sick**. The villages are stuck in a time-warp...

True; but the cities haven't evolved much either. The point is, Ambedkar never forgot how it felt to be excluded and despised. He knew he was going to have to fight deeply entrenched beliefs. He armed himself with an education—at Columbia University and at the London School of Economics. Returning to India, he launched a massive satyagraha in Mahad in 1927. He got dalits to draw water from a tank they had been denied access to. That moment, Ambedkar believed, was as big as the convening of the National Assembly at Versailles in 1789. At Mahad, the dalits rallied to the cry of the French Revolution: Liberty, Equality, Fraternity—ideas that also lie at the heart of Buddhist ethics. Ambedkar spoke to the gathering...

"This meeting is unprecedented. I feel that no parallel to it can be found in the history of India. If we seek for another meeting in the past to equal this, we shall have to go to the history of France: the revolutionary French National Assembly convened in 1789 that set new principles for the organization of society. You are all aware that our Hindu society is based on the system of castes. A rather similar system existed in the France of 1789. The French National Assembly sent the King and Queen of France to the guillotine; persecuted and massacred the aristocrats; and drove their survivors into exile. Whether this social revolution will work peacefully or violently will depend wholly on the conduct of the caste Hindus. People forget that if the rulers of France had not been treacherous to the Assembly, if the upper classes had not resisted it, it would have had no need to use violence in the work of the revolution. We say to our opponents too: Please do not oppose us. Put away the orthodox scriptures. Follow justice."

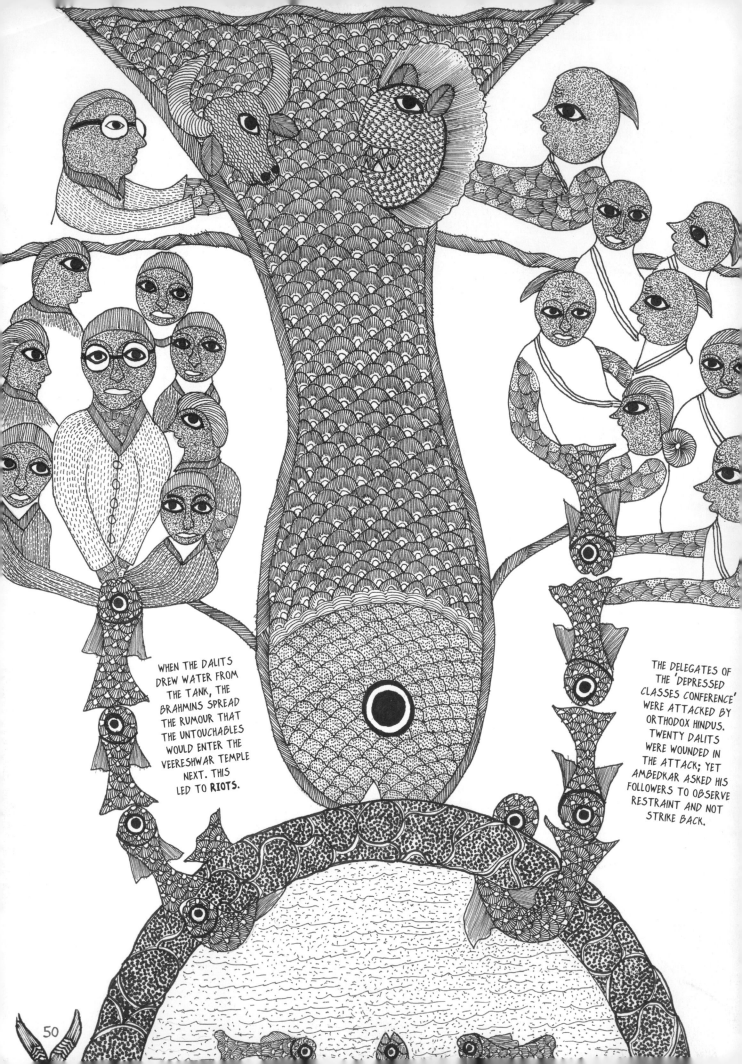

WHEN THE DALITS DREW WATER FROM THE TANK, THE BRAHMINS SPREAD THE RUMOUR THAT THE UNTOUCHABLES WOULD ENTER THE VEERESHWAR TEMPLE NEXT. THIS LED TO **RIOTS**.

THE DELEGATES OF THE 'DEPRESSED CLASSES CONFERENCE' WERE ATTACKED BY ORTHODOX HINDUS. TWENTY DALITS WERE WOUNDED IN THE ATTACK; YET AMBEDKAR ASKED HIS FOLLOWERS TO OBSERVE RESTRAINT AND NOT STRIKE BACK.

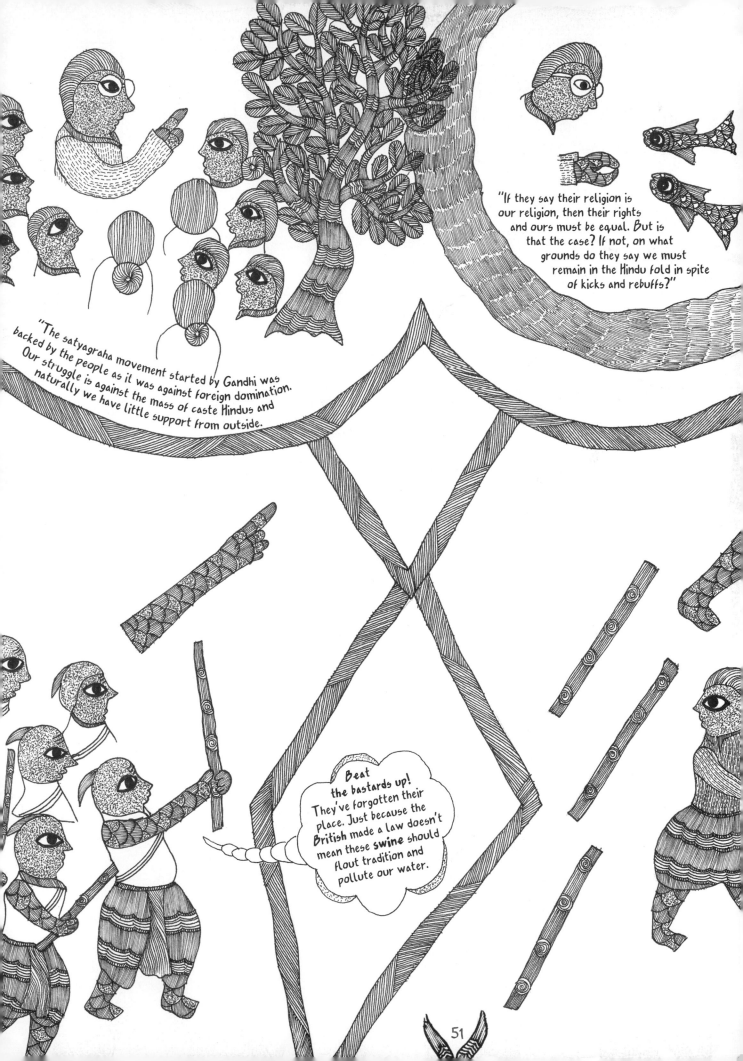

DALIT WORKERS
FOUND SHELTER
IN MUSLIM HOUSES,
AND AMBEDKAR SPENT
THE NIGHT IN A STATE GUEST
HOUSE. IN JUNE 1927, FIVE ORTHODOX
HINDUS WERE SENTENCED BY THE (COLONIAL)
DISTRICT MAGISTRATE TO FOUR MONTHS' RIGOROUS
IMPRISONMENT. AMBEDKAR SAID: 'HAD THE CHIEF
OFFICERS IN THE DISTRICT BEEN HINDUS, JUSTICE
WOULD HAVE BEEN DENIED. UNDER BRAHMIN
PESHWA RULE I **WOULD HAVE BEEN**
TRAMPLED TO DEATH BY
AN ELEPHANT.'

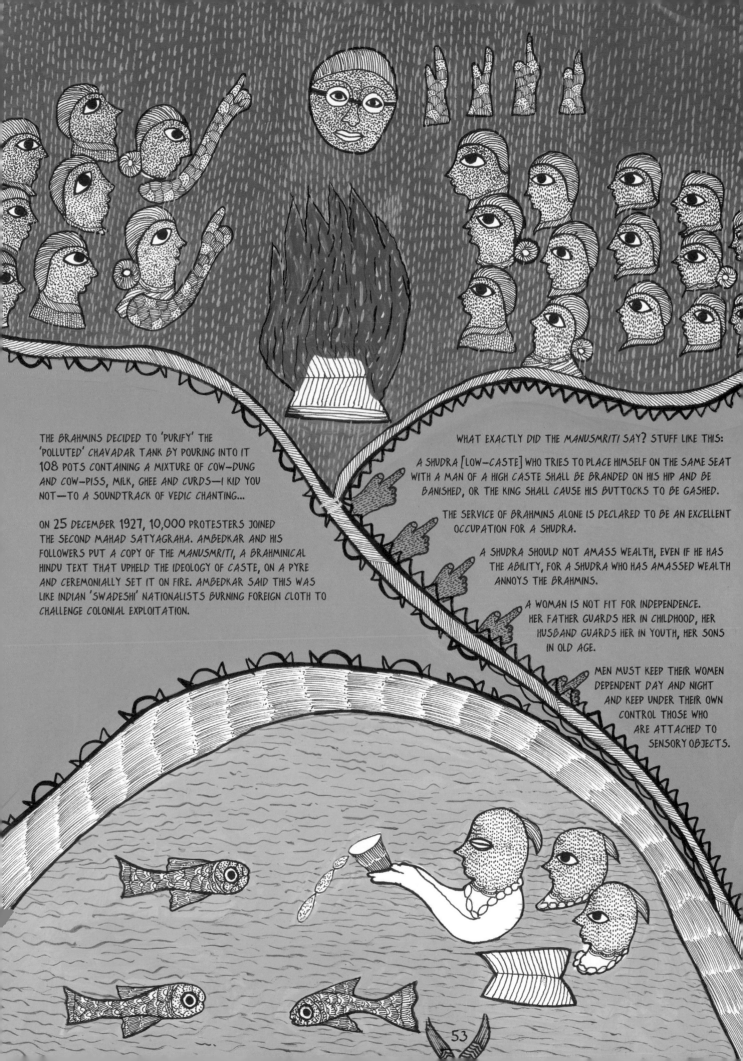

THE BRAHMINS DECIDED TO 'PURIFY' THE 'POLLUTED' CHAVADAR TANK BY POURING INTO IT 108 POTS CONTAINING A MIXTURE OF COW-DUNG AND COW-PISS, MILK, GHEE AND CURDS—I KID YOU NOT—TO A SOUNDTRACK OF VEDIC CHANTING...

ON 25 DECEMBER 1927, 10,000 PROTESTERS JOINED THE SECOND MAHAD SATYAGRAHA. AMBEDKAR AND HIS FOLLOWERS PUT A COPY OF THE MANUSMRITI, A BRAHMINICAL HINDU TEXT THAT UPHELD THE IDEOLOGY OF CASTE, ON A PYRE AND CEREMONIALLY SET IT ON FIRE. AMBEDKAR SAID THIS WAS LIKE INDIAN 'SWADESHI' NATIONALISTS BURNING FOREIGN CLOTH TO CHALLENGE COLONIAL EXPLOITATION.

WHAT EXACTLY DID THE MANUSMRITI SAY? STUFF LIKE THIS:

A SHUDRA [LOW-CASTE] WHO TRIES TO PLACE HIMSELF ON THE SAME SEAT WITH A MAN OF A HIGH CASTE SHALL BE BRANDED ON HIS HIP AND BE BANISHED, OR THE KING SHALL CAUSE HIS BUTTOCKS TO BE GASHED.

THE SERVICE OF BRAHMINS ALONE IS DECLARED TO BE AN EXCELLENT OCCUPATION FOR A SHUDRA.

A SHUDRA SHOULD NOT AMASS WEALTH, EVEN IF HE HAS THE ABILITY, FOR A SHUDRA WHO HAS AMASSED WEALTH ANNOYS THE BRAHMINS.

A WOMAN IS NOT FIT FOR INDEPENDENCE. HER FATHER GUARDS HER IN CHILDHOOD, HER HUSBAND GUARDS HER IN YOUTH, HER SONS IN OLD AGE.

MEN MUST KEEP THEIR WOMEN DEPENDENT DAY AND NIGHT AND KEEP UNDER THEIR OWN CONTROL THOSE WHO ARE ATTACHED TO SENSORY OBJECTS.

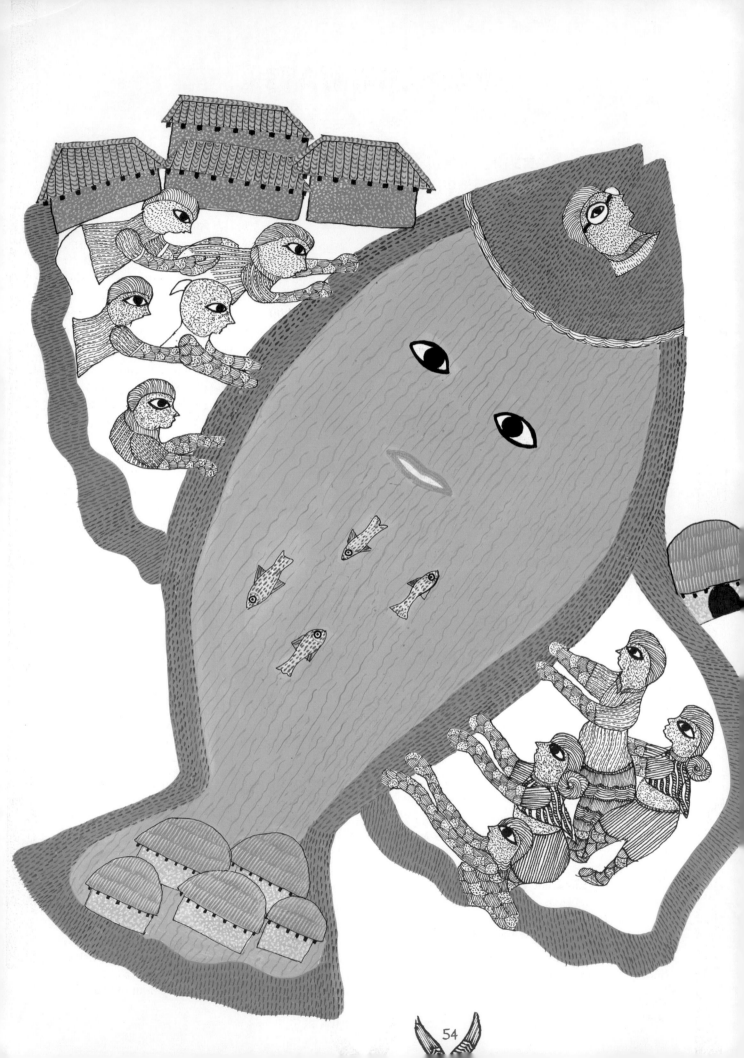

54

SHACKLING WATER

TEHELKA, 26 JAN 2008

WHEN DALITS IN CHAKWARA WON THE RIGHT TO USE THE VILLAGE POND, CASTE HINDUS TURNED IT INTO A SEWER. SALMAN USMANI REPORTS

ON 19 MARCH 1927, one of the first public battles Bhimrao Ramji Ambedkar waged was the satyagraha at Mahad in Maharashtra. He had led 3,000 dalits to assert their right to access the Chavadar Tank at Mahad. Animals were allowed to use the water of the tank but not dalits. The caste Hindus responded to the satyagraha with violence and a social boycott. On 25 December the same year, Ambedkar burnt the *Manusmriti* § the symbol of brahmanic Hinduism that offered scriptural justification for discrimination § at Mahad.

Eighty years later, nothing seems to have changed. Chakwara village, 50 km from Jaipur, bears testimony to this. The village and life in it revolve around a large pond. The pond and its ghats have been built and maintained with state funds and contributions from the entire village, including dalits. The village has about 700 families, of which 70 belong to bairwas who are dalits.

Over 20 years, the village has been in constant turmoil over the curbs dalits face in using the pond. The caste Hindus of Chakwara would not let the bairwas use the pond. However, buffaloes and pigs had unrestricted access.

On 14 December 2001, two bairwas, Babulal and Radheysham, decided to defy the village 'law' and bathed in the pond. Babulal, 54, says his decision to bathe had more to do with the "frustration of being denied clean water, rather than its necessity."

Outraged by this social offence the village Jats and Brahmins surrounded Babulal's house at night and threatened a bloodbath. The next day a panchayat was called which found Babulal and Radheysham guilty of violating the village custom. The panchayat imposed a fine of Rs 50,000 on the bairwa community and demanded a written apology. Further, the upper castes imposed a complete social boycott of the bairwas. They could not buy ration and vegetables from the village shops; no one would employ a bairwa or lend him money; the bairwas were not to use the only handpump in the village.

After continued threats, confrontations and abuses, Babulal finally filed a First Information Report on 22 December 2001. The Jaipur district administration and the police ignored Babulal's complaints and tried to convince the dalits not to use the pond, eventually making some of them sign a compromise agreement. However, the boycott, the threats and the abuse continued for months, with the administration occasionally stepping in only to side with the upper castes.

In September 2002, several human rights organizations collaborated with the bairwas to organize a rally in yet another effort to assert their rights. The upper castes decided to physically confront the rally. They attacked the rally with stones and sticks. The situation worsened and the police responded with teargas and finally had to open fire. Around 50 people were injured, most of whom were policemen. The rally and the confrontation temporarily and unintentionally put the administration and the upper caste men at loggerheads. Complaints were made and pursued in the collector's office.

IT SEEMED LIKE a victory for the bairwas, who started to use the pond regularly, but their triumph was short-lived. Soon after the clash, the upper castes withdrew from the pond. They stopped using it, saying it had become impure. The tension, anger and the boycott has continued since then. However, after the heightened interest of human rights organizations, NGOs, administration, the national and international media, Chakwara and its dalits have fallen off the mindscapes again.

Today, the caste Hindus have started to shit and dump garbage in the pond. Recently, some men dug up the village sewer and directed it to the pond water. Every effort has been made to pollute the pond § literally and symbolically § for now it is only the dalit bairwas who use it.

In urban India, dalits are forced to clean sewers and drains immersing themselves in putrid muck. In Chakwara, a pond that was once considered sacred is now no better than a large sewage tank. The dalits have, after decades, won the right to use it. But they continue to lose their dignity, for the caste Hindus know how to "shackle the rushing form of water".

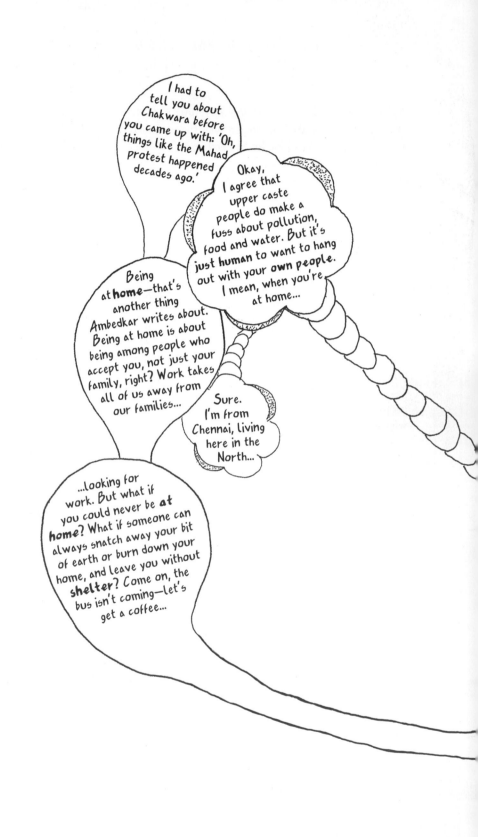

BOOK 2

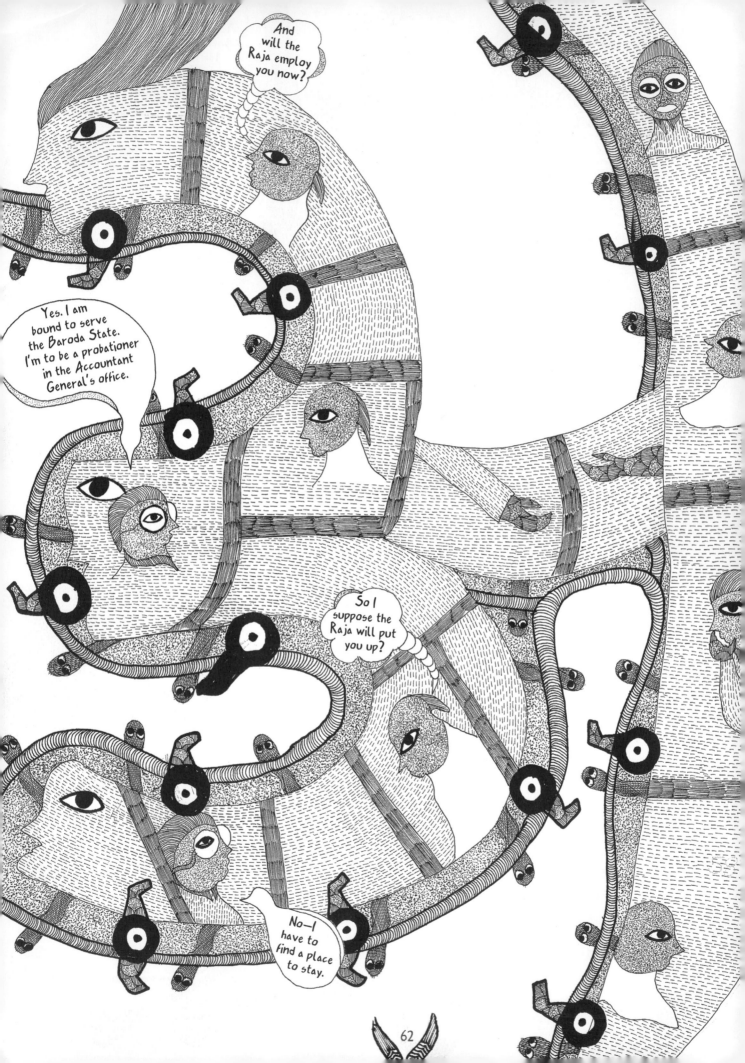

63

65

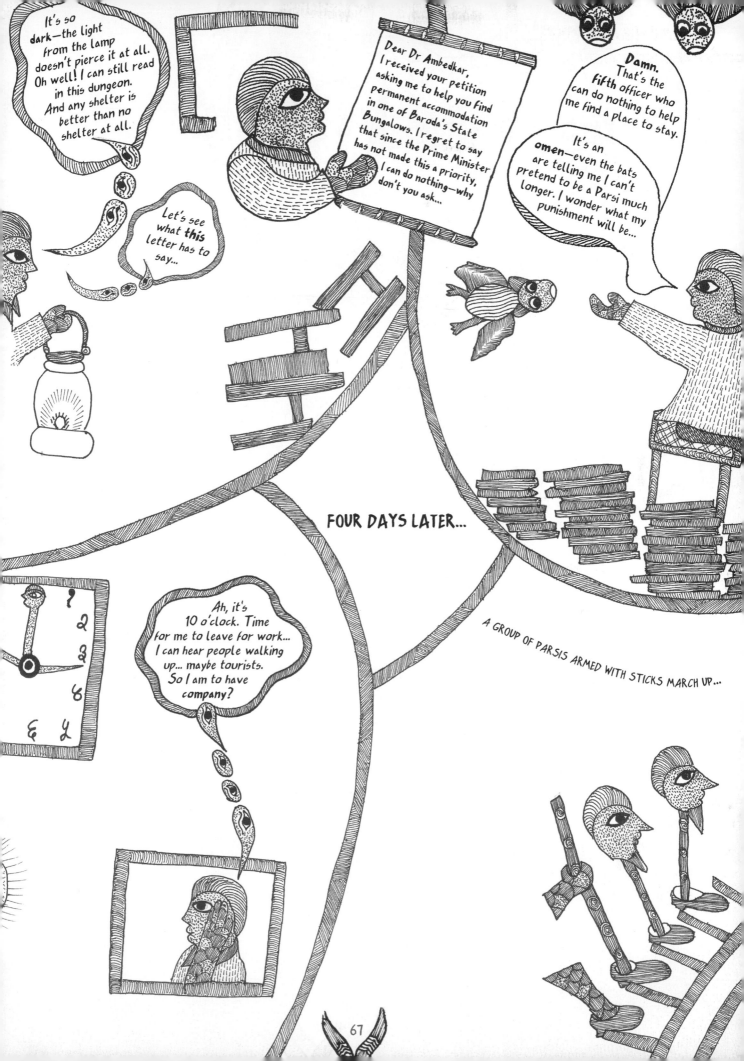

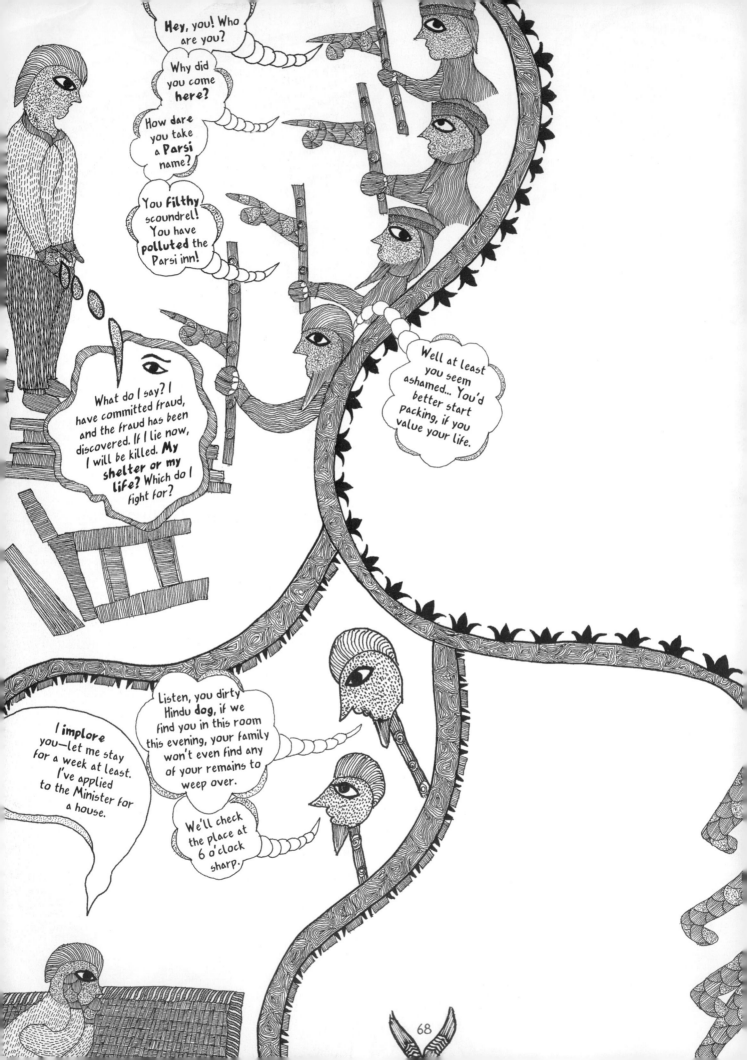

VADODARA,* NAMED FOR THE KINDLY BANYAN TREE,
IN ALL YOUR CROWDED STREETS THERE IS NO PLACE FOR ME.

NO ROOF, NOWHERE TO REST, NO FRIEND WITH WHOM I MIGHT
REHEARSE THE EVENTS OF THE DAY, SPEND AN HOUR OR A NIGHT.

*Vadodara, from vadpatra for banyan,
is the original name of Baroda.

70

"I WONDER WHAT MY PARENTS WOULD HAVE THOUGHT OF ALL THIS. I CAME HERE WITH SUCH HIGH HOPES—I WAS GOING TO PROVE SO MUCH TO THE WORLD, I TURNED DOWN MANY WELL—PAID JOBS TO REPAY MY DEBT TO THE MAHARAJA..."

A while ago you said untouchability exists only in the villages. Ambedkar, because of his caste, was denied shelter in a city like Baroda though he bore all the marks of education and status. In **Delhi**, recently, three students training for the civil service exams were **beaten up** and **evicted** after they were discovered to be dalit.

If the places you call **home** are as bad as this, you can imagine what **travelling** to **new places** might be like...

DALIT SIBLINGS THRASHED BY LANDLORD

THE HINDU
NEW DELHI, 5 May 2008

Three dalit siblings living as tenants in Mukherjee Nagar here were allegedly beaten up and abused by their landlord's family apparently after they learnt of their Scheduled Caste status. Two sisters and a brother living on the third floor of 165 Mukherjee Nagar claimed that they were beaten up and punched by their landlord Om Prakash Grover, his wife, their son and daughter-in-law on Saturday after one of the sisters, Kanaklata, went downstairs to fill water.

"They did not let her fill water and instead started beating her with a slipper. My brother Chandra Bhushan who tried to intervene was also beaten up. On hearing the commotion, I rushed downstairs. They tried to tear my clothes and one of the sons of our landlord punched me. They hurled abuses at us. A number of people had gathered outside the house but no one came forward to help us," claimed Manorama, the other sister.

When the victims called their brother Vijay Bahadur, who stays nearby in a separate accommodation, and a friend, they too were allegedly thrashed by Mr Grover and his family.

BOOK

3

77

"WELL, IT'S PART OF THE NIZAM'S TERRITORY NOW. IT WAS ONCE RULED BY A HINDU KING. THE FORT IS OF GREAT HISTORICAL INTEREST... LET'S TAKE A BREAK AND EAT."

THROWN OUT OF HOSPITAL, TWO DALIT WOMEN DIE

TIMES NEWS NETWORK
2 Nov 2007

KANPUR: If it was expected that atrocities against dalits would become a thing of the past after their icon Mayawati came to power with a Bahujan Samaj Party majority in Uttar Pradesh, it was misplaced because in a shocking incident, two Dalit women died after being thrown out of a government hospital here on Thursday.

The gruesome assault took place because of the inability of the two women to bribe government health officials with a paltry Rs 1,000 each barely two hours after they gave birth to two babies. Devorati (25), who gave birth to a boy around 5 pm, was the first to die. Her husband Dilip had admitted her to the hospital after bribing an official with Rs 500. As per government norms, admission to hospitals is free and women coming for delivery should get Rs 1,400 as an allowance. On the contrary, Dilip was asked to pay an additional Rs 1,000.

Within hours, Kamla, wife of Ramprakash of Ambarpur village, too was thrown out of the hospital just after she gave birth to a girl child when her family members refused to pay a bribe of Rs 500 and instead demanded Rs 1,400 under the Janani-Suraksha Yojna meant for pregnant women in the Below Poverty Line category.

83

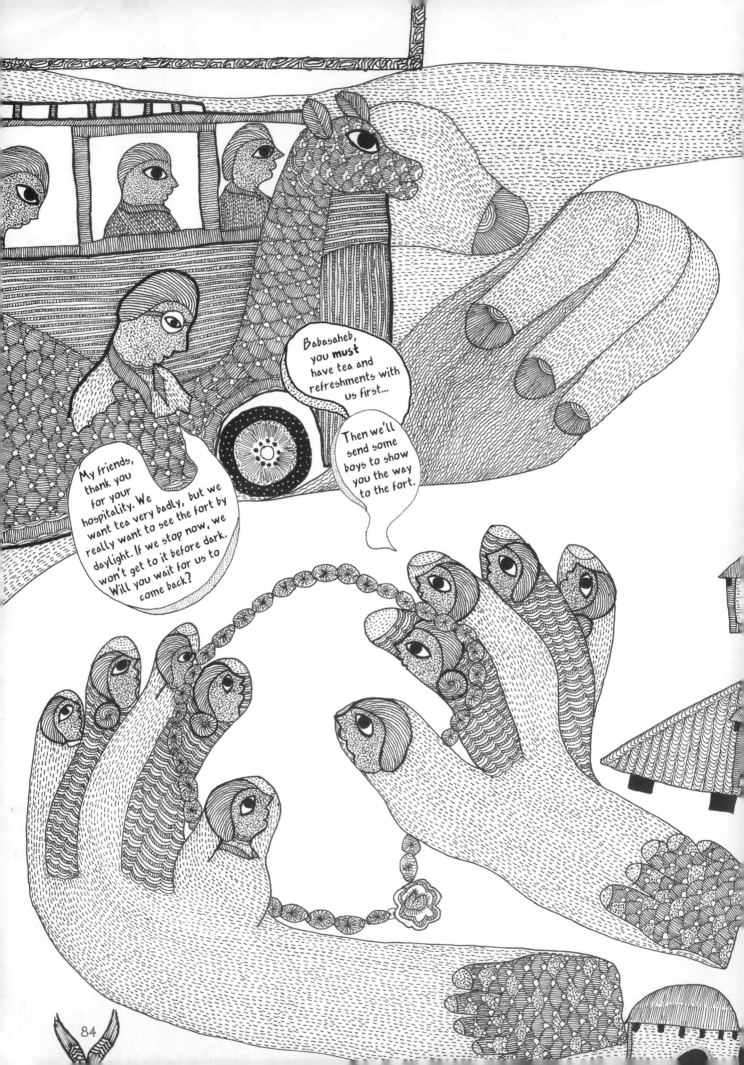

84

A lot of people say we exaggerate the allegations of Hindu injustice, oppression and tyranny. The doctor who treated the untouchable woman, for instance, felt no qualms of conscience in setting aside the code of conduct which is binding on his profession. The Hindu would prefer to be inhuman rather than touch an untouchable. In Baroda I found that a person who is an untouchable to a Hindu is also untouchable to a Parsi. And in Daulatabad I discovered that a person who is an untouchable to a Hindu is also an untouchable to a Mohammedan.

You know, if we take equality and social justice at all seriously in this country today, it's thanks to **Ambedkar.**

You're exaggerating, right? Next you'll be saying Ambedkar was more serious about equality than **Gandhi!**

I'd say that without hesitation. Ambedkar campaigned for a just society all his life, from the time he launched an anticaste newspaper in 1920, through the years he spent studying at the London School of Economics and qualifying at Gray's Inn to be a lawyer, through the years he spent practising law at the Bombay High Court. He wanted the untouchable castes to be politicized, to fight for their rights, not to have to rely on the kindness and good intentions of upper-caste Hindus. He launched organizations to raise political awareness and to build schools and libraries for the most marginalized castes. Gandhi had different priorities—he was more concerned with India's freedom from British rule than with the transformation of Hindu society.

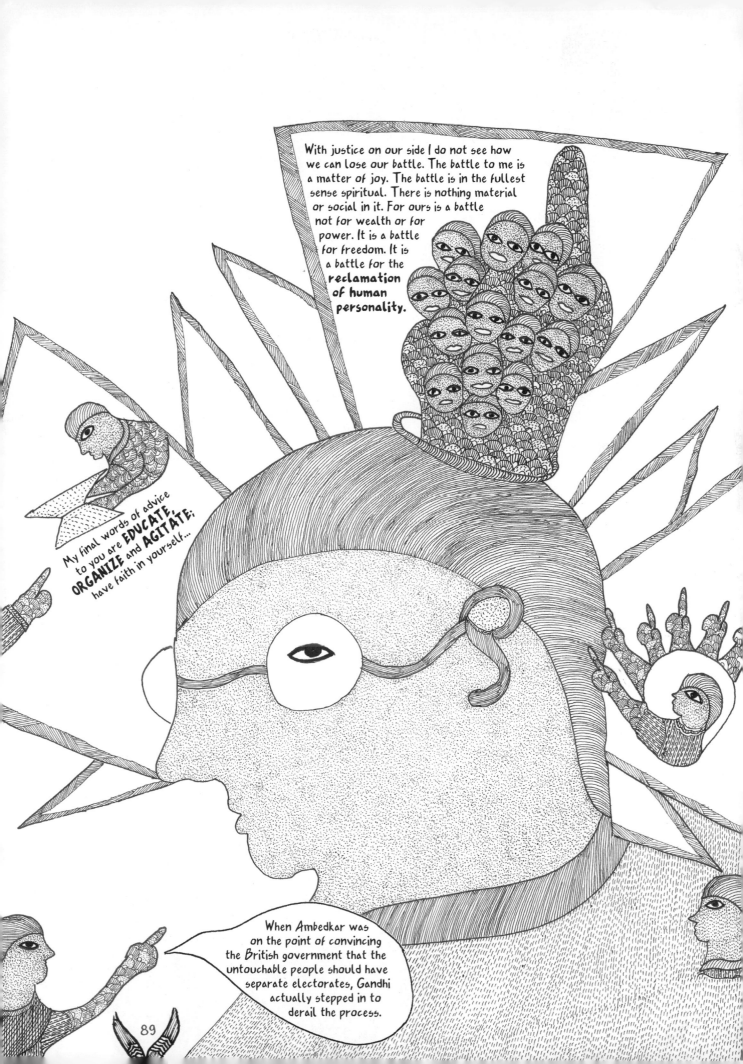

September 1931

To the Minorities Committee of the Indian Round Table Conference

The following are the terms and conditions on which the Depressed Classes will consent to place themselves under a majority rule in a self-governing India.

1. EQUAL CITIZENSHIP

2. FREE ENJOYMENT OF EQUAL RIGHTS

3. PROTECTION AGAINST DISCRIMINATION

4. ADEQUATE REPRESENTATION IN LEGISLATURES

5. ADEQUATE REPRESENTATION IN THE SERVICES

6. ADEQUATE REPRESENTATION IN CABINET

7. REDRESS AGAINST PREJUDICIAL ACTION

I have not the slightest doubt that if the Untouchables of India were given the chance of electing their representatives to this Conference, I would find a place here. I say therefore that **I fully represent the claims of my community.** Let no man be under any mistaken impression as regards that.

So Gandhi, with his fast, twisted the government's arm as well as Ambedkar's, and the government shelved the idea of independent electorates. Ambedkar said: 'The Congress sucked the juice out and threw the rind in the face of the untouchables.'

Hmm... Independent electorates would be a bit like **reservation** in jobs, right? I'm with Gandhi on this one.

I'm sure you are. Just as I'm sure that if anyone but Ambedkar had drafted free India's national **Constitution,** it would have been a very different document.

That's the one thing they taught me about Ambedkar in school—that he was the architect of the Constitution. Wasn't he Chair of the—uh—the Something Committee?

—the Drafting Committee. The draft Constitution that the Constituent Assembly adopted in 1949 was mostly his doing.

WE, THE PEOPLE OF INDIA, having solemnly resolved to constitute India into a SOVEREIGN DEMOCRATIC REPUBLIC and to secure to all its citizens: JUSTICE, social, economic and political; LIBERTY of thought, expression, belief, faith and worship; EQUALITY of status and of opportunity; and to promote among them all FRATERNITY assuring the dignity of the individual and the unity of the Nation; IN OUR CONSTITUENT ASSEMBLY this twenty-sixth day of November, 1949, do HEREBY ADOPT, ENACT AND GIVE TO OURSELVES THIS CONSTITUTION.

I claim myself in my own person to represent the vast mass of the Untouchables. I claim that I would get, if there was a referendum of the untouchables, their vote, and that **I would top the poll!**

March 1932

To Sir Samuel Hoare, Secretary of State for India

Dear Sir Samuel,

The Untouchables are not well organized. There is very little political consciousness among them and they are so horribly treated that I want to save them against themselves. I hold that a separate electorate is harmful for the Depressed Classes and for Hinduism. I therefore respectfully inform His Majesty's Government that in the event of their decision creating a separate electorate for the Depressed Classes, I must fast unto death...

I remain, your faithful friend, M.K. Gandhi

1. The State shall not discriminate against any citizen on grounds only of religion, race, caste, sex, place of birth.

2. No citizen shall, on grounds only of religion, race, caste, sex, place of birth be subject to any disability, liability, restriction or condition with regard to—

a) access to shops, public restaurants, hotels and places of public entertainment; or

b) the use of wells, tanks, bathing ghats, roads and places of public resort maintained wholly or partly out of State funds or dedicated to the use of the general public.

3. Nothing in this article shall prevent the State from making any special provision for women and children.

Did you know Ambedkar was **India's First Law Minister?** His draft of the **Hindu Code Bill** tried to make Hindu personal law more equitable, especially for women. The Bill sanctioned **divorce**, for instance, and expanded the **property rights of widows and girl children.** The Constituent Assembly debated it for months, and ended up rejecting not only Ambedkar's draft but also a second, watered-down one. He was too far ahead of his time. He was so outraged he resigned from Nehru's cabinet.

That must have been quite a statement.

91

BOOK

4

I am **Durga**. I was born in Barbaspur village in eastern Madhya Pradesh. Near our village is the Dhooti jungle, so called because it is structured like a bamboo fish basket. Here, I am 10 years old, listening to the bedtime stories my grandma tells me.

Every morning, I'd head to the Tudar river, wash, bathe and fetch water. I would then sweep the yard and make digna with the white chuhi matti (earth). I would pat cow dung into cakes. Then off to the Tudar again to fetch more water, catch some fish with nets made of coarse cloth and collect firewood from the Dhooti.

When Anand approached me for the Ambedkar book, I suggested Subhash and I would work together on this. He agreed and we made several trips to Delhi and he visited us in Bhopal several times.

During one of our visits to Navayana, Anand was not in the office and the landlady abused us and wouldn't let us go in. She said we looked like yokels. That hurt us. Anand told her that I was an artist who had published many books and had even been to Frankfurt, but none of this made any difference to her. We were reminded of Ambedkar's plight in Baroda and could understand his hurt.

A Digna for Bhim

During one of the first sessions I had with Durgabai Vyam and Subhash Vyam, sometime in June 2008, they browsed the books of the masters of the graphic book genre, North American, Franco-Belgian and Japanese—Will Eisner, Art Spiegelman, Joe Sacco, Shaun Tan and Osamu Tezuka. They also looked at Marjane Satrapi's *Persepolis* and the work of some Indian graphic novelists. The Vyams counterposed their own philosophy of art to the visual imagery in these graphic texts (which they described as being by 'fine art school' types): 'We'd like to state one thing very clearly at the outset. We shall not force our characters into boxes. It stifles them. We prefer to mount our work in open spaces. Our art is *khulla* (open) where there's space for all to breathe.' This was a defining moment—we were on to something that would defy the conventional grammar of graphic books. Tiresome photorealism was out of the question. Nor would the Vyams offer cinematic establishment shots, close-ups or extreme close-ups (of tense hands, surprised eyes, furrowed brow), mid-shot, perspective, light and shadow, three dimensionality, aerial views, low angles etc that have come to constitute the mise-en-scène of graphic books. The same character might not appear similar through the book. Durgabai had worked on several picture books, especially for children, but the Vyams or other Gond artists had never explored sequential art. Even when they 'illustrated' children's books, they were known for their full-page renditions.

In fact, since the mid-1990s, once the Pardhan Gond art movement was established by Jangarh Singh Shyam who blazed a trail from his eastern Madhya Pradesh village of Patangarh to Bharat Bhavan in Bhopal, the Pompidou in Paris and the Mithila Museum (of all places) in Niigata, rural Japan, some publishers had begun to extensively use Gond art to illustrate children's books. At Navayana, I had commissioned Durgabai Vyam for a nonfiction book for children in 2007. Durga and Subhash had said then: 'Get us to work on something we have never done before, and on a large scale.' As I became more familiar with the history of the Pardhan Gond art form and its contemporary moorings, I began to comprehend the range, complexity and depth of this genre of artistic expression. I needed to present the Vyams with a challenge that did justice to their sophisticated visual language.

> I am the bird speech bubble. My other friends and I appear only for characters whose speech is soft, the lovable characters, the victims of caste—men and women who speak like birds.

Jangarh's Legacy

Before we go further, a brief overview of the origins of Pardhan Gond art is necessary for those who are experiencing their approach for the first time here. Pardhan Gonds, a clan belonging to the larger Gond tribal community in central India, serve as the traditional keepers of their people's cultural heritage and lineages—remembering family genealogies, and transmitting legends, sacred myths and oral histories through songs and storytelling. Pardhan Gond bards are still patronized by the larger Gond community, yet – with customary tribal patronage dwindling over the past century – their traditional livelihood and performance narratives have been made increasingly obsolete.

In the early-1980s, artist Jagdish Swaminathan (1928–1994) – then director of Bhopal's newly founded Charles Correa-designed Bharat Bhavan cultural centre – sent scouts into rural Madhya Pradesh, where one of them spotted the talent of Jangarh Singh Shyam in remote Patangarh. Swaminathan immediately recognized Jangarh's genius and encouraged him to become a professional artist. Since then many Pardhan Gonds have followed in his footsteps. Thus Pardhan songs and oral traditions, which had for centuries been recited to accompany performances on the *bana* (a sacred fiddle), began to be depicted on paper and canvas, as well as in prominent mural commissions—such as on the facade of Madhya Pradesh's legislative assembly building, and on the domes of Bharat Bhavan (now weathered out). At Bharat Bhavan itself, Swaminathan ensured that the works by Pardhan Gonds occupied pride of place alongside the best creations of non-tribal, urban-

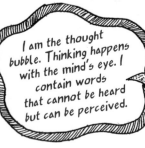

> I am the thought bubble. Thinking happens with the mind's eye. I contain words that cannot be heard but can be perceived.

100

bound artists. This contemporary expression of Pardhan Gond art has been termed *Jangarh Kalam*, Jangarh Idiom, by poet Udayan Vajpeyi.

In 2001, Jangarh committed suicide under murky circumstances while working as an artist-in-residence at the Mithila Museum in Niigata, rural Japan. By then he had already brought to Bhopal's Professors Colony a wide array of Gond artists, among whom was the married couple Durgabai Vyam and Subhash Vyam (whose sister Nankusia married Jangarh). They, in turn, continued to encourage other Gonds from their village and urban communities to seek a livelihood as professional visual artists, and have generously offered guidance and informal instruction from their modest home and workplace in Bhopal. For instance, during the making of this book, while nine persons lived in the Vyams' two-room household, including Subhash's nephew Sukhnandi Vyam and his family, there would be at least six visitors camping there—doing art, looking for work or just smoking marijuana. 'On a daily basis, 5 kilos of rice and 3 kilos of wheat flour are required in our kitchen,' Subhash once told me. It is the compulsion of supporting such large families that forces major artists like Durgabai or Subhash to be labeled 'craftspersons' and be huddled in 'tribal artist camps' in Delhi or Bangalore where they are offered sometimes a measly Rs 1,000 per day (USD 22) for doing hatched fish-scale patterns on a piece of paper, canvas, or – as it turned out once during the making of the book – paint on metal vases. The approach of some well-networked art aficionados in Delhi is sometimes no different from that of Nike's sweatshops in Vietnam. Tribal-origin artists – even when they can hold their own with their urban compatriots – are relegated to doing the decorative for a daily wage. After all, Jangarh Shyam, when he died in 2001 at the age of 40, was working for just Rs 12,000 a month in the alienating atmosphere of the Mithila Museum run by Tokio Hasegawa. According to art historian Yashodhara Dalmia, a backpacking Hasegawa stumbled upon the animated paintings of Madhubani artists in the 1980s, realized their worth, set up a lucrative business by importing these priceless works to Japan and eventually established a 'museum' in rural Japan. When I approached the Vyams, I was conscious of this history of exploitation that continues to this day.

In the course of producing *Bhimayana*, Navayana facilitated an exhibition for the brilliant young sculptor Sukhnandi Vyam (Subhash' nephew) at the Wieden+Kennedy gallery in Delhi (March–April 2010). The 17 pieces on display were priced between Rs 80,000 and Rs 2.5 lakh. Not one was sold, but a major statement had been made about the dignity of the artist. A contemporary (non-tribal) artist in Delhi, a self-styled 'collector of tribal art' who has even managed to put together a private museum, said she had been used to buying Gond and other tribal art works for Rs 500. Sukhnandi's show seemed to have shocked and disoriented her. Such exploiters lament the loss of 'innocence of tribal artists' and their 'commercialisation'.

Framing Bhimayana

Just as the unlettered Vyams were unfamiliar with contemporary graphic books, they were unaware of Ambedkar. Their daughter Roshni, 14, an emerging artist – who has done the fish-style font and the numbers used for chapter headings – knew the basic facts though. She told them about the 'guy in the statue in the New Market area with one hand extended, index finger pointing to something afar, another hand holding a book.' Over several sessions, I narrated to them the storyboard, improvising with each telling. I left them with a hand-written Hindi version, for Roshni to read aloud and explain to them. I told them that the text was only a guide to give a sense of direction and they were free to do what they wished. Each brainstorming threw up new insights and also new dead-ends.

Soon, the Vyams were making Ambedkar's story their own. The humiliations Ambedkar faced affected them deeply. They were moved and angered. They internalized the stories. They began cutting out reports of Khairlanji-like incidents from the local papers. By April 2009, the first set of drawings emerged—they turned out to be all full-page works. As promised, there were no panels. Nor would they follow any of the storyboard's technical 'instructions'. We printed a 16-page sampler from the first section of the Water chapter where Bhim is denied water in school. A series of full-page

I am full of words that carry a sting. Characters who love caste, whose words contain poison, whose touch is venomous, speak through me.

Sukhnandi Vyam's "Artist"

101

drawings made it appear like a picture book and threatened to result in an unwieldy and unaffordable 400-pager. We had to come up with an innovative way of panelling and yet not impose the tyranny of conventional panels, without compromising on the credo of not forcing people into boxes. After several frustrating and failed attempts, and months of brainstorming, one muggy Sunday afternoon in August 2009 Subhash suggested that we use the digna – the traditional auspicious design patterns applied to walls and floors in Gond homes – as a way of dividing up a page. He showed me how in rough sketches. A eureka moment! I hugged him. It is in the digna that the origins of Pardhan Gond practice of art lay. Jangarh Singh's murals that now adorn the walls of the Pompidou Centre, or the Bharat Bhavan and the Vidhan Sabha (legislative assembly) buildings in Bhopal originate from the seemingly simple digna. To the left of this page you will see one of the digna patterns that, with subtle variations, forms a leitmotif *Bhimayana*. Sometimes, entire pages bear this pattern (34–37); at other times deft variations adorn panel borders (22, 28).

The ecology of Pardhan Gond art is such that even when dealing with urban subjects we see freefalling animals, birds and trees in landscapes without a horizon. The train becomes a snake, the intimidating fort a lion. The happiness of the people of Chalisgaon who receive Babasaheb Ambedkar (79) is not conveyed through smiling faces but a dancing peacock. An earthmover used by a dalit, who is killed for digging a well, sheds tears as two cows bear witness (46). As Sirish Rao and Gita Wolf write in the introduction to Bhajju Shyam's *The London Jungle Book* (2005), Gond art does not represent, it signifies. Very early on, the Vyams saw thirsty young Bhim as a fish (17, 19). When I realized that the Vyams loved portraying aquatic life, I suggested they could consider framing some pages like a fish. On page 25, a water tank whose construction young Bhim's father is supervising in Goregaon appears like a fish, as does the common village tank in Satara, fins making room for narrative text. In the preceding page, fishes zero in towards the centre and the Vyams offer an organic approach to paneling. The entire Chakwara story (54) becomes a fish. Ambedkar's historic Mahad speech on the dalit's basic human right to access water reaches the audience through loudspeakers that act as sprinklers—here we see one of the most imaginative and original uses of gutter space in the history of modern graphic art (48). In the next chapter, when a homeless Ambedkar ruminates over his fate in Baroda's Kamathi Garden, he becomes the park (68).

On several occasions Durga and Subhash would introduce narrative elements, situations and characters not provided for in the storyboard. So much that close to 40 percent of the text and dialogue was generated or re-edited to suit the drawings. For instance, page 82 has a neighing horse and four furious faces. In the previous panel, the sister-in-law of Namdeo (the first-time cart driver) blames the horse for tripping the cart and defends her kin. Durga says the horse would surely laugh at this. On page 66, Ambedkar's plight in Baroda is depicted like those of oxen that harness the oil-press, walking in circles and going nowhere. Each time you view a page in this book, you will discover new ways of seeing, new meanings, new pleasures, fresh insights.

Ambedkar's Missing Story

Navayana was launched in 2003 with *Ambedkar: Autobiographical Notes*, a little 36-page book priced at Rs 40 (about 1 USD back then). In the multi-volume *Babasaheb Ambedkar: Writings and Speeches*, edited by Vasant Moon, these writings can be found in Volume 12 under the title "Waiting for a Visa". The connection between the title and the six autobiographical 'illustrations' – as Ambedkar calls them – is not clear. Perhaps, Ambedkar intended adding more to this body of writing – of less than 10,000 words – but eventually could not. All that the editorial note by Moon says is: 'Here are some of the reminiscences drawn by Dr. Ambedkar in his own handwriting. The MSS traced in the collection of the People's Education Society were published by the society as a booklet on 19th March 1990.—ed.' If these are *some* reminiscences, were there more? What visa was Ambedkar waiting for? We can, however, gather from the content that Ambedkar wrote at least a few of these available notes in 1935. In the second reminiscence, he refs to his return from London to work in Baroda in 1917. Towards the end of this section, he recalls that '18 years has not succeeded in fading away' the memory of the incidence of untouchability he experienced in the Parsi inn in Baroda. It is clear that Ambedkar jotted down several such 'illustrations' over the years, and perhaps many have been lost.

In the storyboard, Srividya Natarajan stuck to Ambedkar's versions of the episodes in letter and spirit but also created new characters and scenarios. In the first two chapters (Water and Shelter) the episodes drawn from Ambedkar's "Waiting for a Visa" are dated accurately, whereas some liberties have been taken with the dates of the events in the Travel chapter. The Mahad satyagraha story does not figure in "Visa", but was included because of its thematic connection. The Gandhi–Ambedkar confrontation at the Round Table Conference in 1931–32, the drafting of the Constitution and Ambedkar's turn to Buddhism have been included to give a sense of completion to Ambedkar's story.

In India today, as in the rest of the world, few outside the dalit movement are familiar with these experiences of Ambedkar. India's hidden apartheid has unfortunately not become a global concern. One of the iconic moments in the global history of anticolonial struggles is considered to be when, in 1893, a 24-year-old Mohandas Karamchand Gandhi is thrown out of the first-class compartment of a train in Pietermaritzburg, South Africa, and he is, in his own words, 'accommodated in a tin compartment where Kaffirs are packed like sheep.' This incident – the horror of being 'degraded' to the level of 'bestial Kaffirs' – is believed to have spurred Gandhi towards his lifelong and tenacious struggle against colonial authority and discrimination. That Gandhi, as a resourceful young lawyer, could afford a first-class ticket in a foreign country is lost sight of. That Gandhi had to go all the way to South Africa to discover racial discrimination, whereas young Bhimrao encountered this as a 10-year-old in Satara, Bombay Presidency, in 1901, is forgotten.

In 1895, when Gandhi encounters two doors to the Durban post office – one for whites and the other shared by Indians and black Africans – he finds it offensive. In 'an appeal to the Indian public' on 14 August 1896, he laments the fate of 100,000 British Indians in South Africa: 'In the Durban Post and Telegraph offices there were separate entrances for natives and Asiatics, and Europeans. We felt the indignity too much and many respectable Indians were insulted and called all sorts of names by the clerks at the counter. We petitioned the authorities to do away with the invidious distinction and they have now provided three separate entrances for natives, Asiatics, and Europeans.' While touchable Gandhi who succeeded in furthering the cause of racial segregation in South Africa came to be recognized as a global anti-imperialism icon, untouchable Bhim who could not drink water in his local school and went on to lead the Mahad satyagraha in 1927 has been neglected by history.

Ambedkar talks of experiencing social equality for the first time in his life during his years in Columbia University; once back in India he is constantly reminded of his untouchability. For Gandhi, the script was played out in the opposite way—the experience of discrimination had to happen far from the social security and comfort that India provides its touchable classes. Today, the same Indian elite that bemoans racial violence and discrimination in Australia snuffs out the lives of two dalits every day. According to the National Crime Records Bureau's statistics for 2008, a crime is committed against a dalit every 18 minutes. On this, there's a chilling silence.

Bhimayana is a small effort to address this anomaly and make Ambedkar's story universal. If the lives and experiences of Martin Luther King and Rosa Parks, Nelson Mandela and Malcolm X could resonate universally, Ambedkar's – and those of millions of dalits in India – ought to as well. After this 'unusually beautiful' rendering of Bhim's story by Durgabai Vyam and Subhash Vyam, there can be no reason not to engage.

Jai Bhim!

S. Anand

I started making dignas at the age of six—using different kinds of clay to draw colourful patterns on walls during festivals and weddings. I've done art work for several books, primarily for children. *The Night Life of Trees*, coauthored by me, won the BolognaRagazzi Award in 2008. I have handled a wide range of themes—from our Gond gods to the horror of the Bhopal gas leak. I really enjoyed drawing Ambedkar's life along with my husband Subhash. While doing the book I once told Anand, this is like the *Ramayana*! He said, 'No, this is **Bhimayana**'—and that's how we hit upon this title.

DURGABAI VYAM

SUBHASH VYAM

I should say something about myself? Sorry, my number's always busy. Ok, wait... I started working with clay at the age of 10. I used to sculpt in wood. I gave that up since there were no buyers for bulky sculpture. I've since been doing paintings on canvas and paper. Once we cracked a way of doing the panels, the Ambedkar project gave us a lot of scope to experiment with—fusing colours with black for instance. This is my first book and I'm glad Durga and I did this together.

SRIVIDYA NATARAJAN

I was born in Chennai, India, and now live in London, Canada, and teach English and Creative Writing at King's University College. I trained as a Bharatanatyam dancer, and I've illustrated books for children. My first novel, *No Onions Nor Garlic* (2006), was a comic satire on caste. I storyboarded Jotirao Phule's *Slavery* as a graphic book, *A Gardener in the Wasteland*. I'm now working on my second novel, *Undoing Dance*.

I'd been a journalist for ten years. Late in 2003, in a moment of madness, and conspiring with my lend-an-idea friend Ravikumar, we started Navayana. He sat me on a tiger and I haven't been able to get off it. It was Ravi who planted the idea of an imaginative visual treatment of Ambedkar's "Waiting for a Visa" in my head.

S. ANAND

APARAJITA NINAN

As a graphic design student, I worked as an intern with Navayana in 2009–10 towards the graphic novel, *A Gardener in the Wasteland: Jotirao Phule's Fight for Liberty*. I enjoyed creating the font 'Bhim' for this book.

This work would not have been possible
without the support of

Tara Brace-John, Linda van der Gaag, Isha Aggarwal,
Akila Seshasayee, Joe Sacco, John Berger, Arundhati Roy

Sukhnandi Vyam, Durgesh Vyam, Roshni Vyam, Santosh Dhurve,
Rajni Vyam, Mansingh Vyam, Saroj Vyam, Sachin Vyam
in Bhopal

Sadanand Menon, the late Dilip Chitre, Aruna Rathnam,
Raja Mohanty, Mridula Koshy, Meena Kandasamy,
Jitendra Kumar, R. Sivapriya, Jerry Pinto

First published in January 2011
14 12 10 9 11 13
ISBN 9788189059170

Published in Malayalam, Kannada, Tamil, Telugu, Hindi, Marathi,
French, Spanish and Korean

Typeset in *Bhim* at Navayana

Published by Navayana Publishing Pvt Ltd
155, Second Floor, Shahpur Jat, New Delhi 110049
www.navayana.org

Printed and bound by Sanjiv Palliwal, New Delhi, India